MINING IN
CORNWALL
1850-1960

Volume Two

J. H. Trounson
on behalf of the Trevithick Society

Dyllansow Truran

© J.H. Trounson, 1980

Published 1980 by
Moorland Publishing Co Ltd
ISBN 0903485 79 6

This edition published 1989 by
Dyllansow Truran,
Trewolsta, Trewirgie,
Redruth, Cornwall
ISBN 1 85022 049 2

Printed in Great Britain by
Bath Press, Bath

MINES IN CORNWALL

MAP 2

MINES IN THE
ST JUST-CAMBORNE AREA

St Just to Camborne

St Just, in the extreme west of Cornwall, is one of its oldest, if not the oldest mining district, and it is widely believed to be the home of underground mining in the west. As early as the sixteenth century the first attempts were made to work the tin lodes which outcropped on the cliffs, by means of adits or tunnels driven inland from just above sea level. As the workings progressed shafts were sunk to improve ventilation and for access, and, as pumping machinery became available, the shafts were sunk below adit.

Small mines predominated on the coast, in an almost unbroken chain running from south of Cape Cornwall to Morvah, Zennor, St Ives and Lelant. Here and there were a few larger concerns, such as St Just United Mine, which was in 1869 the first limited liability mining company in Cornwall to pay a dividend. Larger still were Botallack Mine, and Levant Mine, now part of Geevor Mine, which also has the county's first mining museum. Further east lay St Ives Consolidated, and the Providence Mines. Another important area for copper and tin comprised the parishes of Marazion, St Hilary, Perranuthnoe, Germoe and Breage. Here again numerous small works predomominated, with one or two large ones such as Tregurtha Downs Mine, Great Work Mine, and Great Wheal Vor (wheal meaning a mine); the last named was in its time the biggest tin mine in Cornwall. At Roseworthy were the hammer mills and the English Arsenic Company's refinery, two important works which depended on the mining industry.

1 The engines of the St Just United Mine on the cliffs above Priest's Cove, about 1863, with local fishing boats in the foreground hauled up for safety above high tide mark by means of a capstan. In the distance can be seen Land's End.

2

2   Bailey's Engine Shaft of St Just United is in the foreground and the engine-houses of Cape Cornwall Mine can be seen on the southern side of the Cape, to the left of the picture. The headgear and pumping engine-house of the latter mine are visible at the south-western tip of the Cape. The little chimney stack on the highest point of Cape Cornwall is a well-known landmark for ships but it is, unfortunately, now in a bad state of repair after having withstood the gales for more than a century. The draught from this stack, so high above the boiler-house, was found to be so excessive that it was later found necessary to build another short chimney on the hill-side just above the engine-house. The sea in this very old photograph (again about 1863) appears peculiarly flat and motionless, the reason being that the picture was taken on one of the old 'wet-plate' negatives which required such a lengthy exposure that the waves moved an appreciable distance during the time that the camera shutter was open.

3   Cape Cornwall again, probably in the 1870s, but this time at low tide. The boiler flue from the beam winding engine (left of centre) can be seen climbing up over the hill to connect with the stack. The building to the right of the winding engine is the 'Count-House' or office of the mine, and the small round house with a

conical roof, still further to the right, is the gunpowder house or magazine which was usually built in this form on Cornish mines.

4 'Coffins', or ancient surface workings, near St Just United with small headgears and a 'horse whim' (or winding machine) of a later generation of miners on the skyline, photographed in the late nineteenth century.

5 The Crowns section of the famous Botallack Mine, thought to have been photographed in the 1860s. In its day it was regarded as one of the wonders of the world and even today the ruined engine-houses are a remarkable sight. The lower engine-house is that of the pumping engine on the Crowns Engine Shaft (this was a singularly dry mine in spite of its situation beneath the ocean). The engine-house in the centre of the picture contained the winding engine which wound from the celebrated Diagonal Shaft, the top of which was further down the cliff face. This was sunk for 2,616 ft at an angle of $32\frac{1}{2}$ degrees from the horizontal so that at its greatest depth it was 1,360 ft below sea level, the workings extending 2,580 ft beyond the cliffs. Amongst the illustrious visitors to the workings were Queen Victoria in 1846 and the Prince and Princess of Wales (or, as Cornishmen would prefer to say, the Duke and Duchess of Cornwall) in 1865.

5

6

6   The timber staging supporting the rails on which the 'skip' ran from the winding engine down to the mouth of the Diagonal Shaft, which appears as a small black hole in the cliff at the bottom end of the staging. This scene is thought to have been photographed in the 1860s.

7   Before reliable steel wire winding ropes became available iron chains were commonly used for hoisting in mine shafts. In April 1863 the chain used in the Diagonal Shaft at Botallack Mine broke and nine miners met their death at the bottom of the shaft. This disaster led to the painting of a famous picture entitled 'From under the Sea' by C. J. Hook RA which was exhibited at the Royal Academy in 1864. The original is now in the Manchester Art Gallery. In order to paint such a realistic picture the artist must have actually visited the scene. It depicts miners in the wheeled skip who have just arrived back safely at the surface after the lengthy journey up through the Diagonal Shaft and who are being welcomed by a young wife and her children — melodrama in the best Victorian tradition! (*Photo: Manchester Art Gallery*)

8 July 24 1865 was a memorable day in the long and colourful history of Botallack Mine for it was then that the Prince and Princess of Wales (later King Edward VII and Queen Alexandra) descended the Diagonal Shaft and examined some of the deep workings of this famous tin and copper mine. This photograph does not show the Royal visitors but the other members of the party who went down in the next skip. Note the decorative flowering bushes arranged for the occasion! Unfortunately the bottom of the negative must have been damaged and the photographer has retouched it so that the iron rails on which the skip ran do not appear in front of the vehicle. Everything was perched on or over the cliff edge, even the capstan on the right for raising and lowering heavy items in the pumping shaft.

9 The earliest working of Botallack is believed to have been at least as long ago as 1721, but the mine finally closed down in March 1895 at a time when the price of tin had fallen to an exceptionally low level. This photograph was taken at the time that the machinery on the Crowns section of the mine was being dismantled and forms a sad contrast to the earlier pictures taken in the 1860s.

9

10 In 1907 the Botallack mines were reopened and it was decided to lower an electric sinking pump in Wheal Cock Engine Shaft on the other side of the headland. The top part of the shaft was very close to the cliff and to make it secure it was necessary to build a massive masonry wall to a considerable height and to form a circular 'collar' for the shaft made of stones from the old engine-house. The photograph shows the work in progress, the foundations of the old building being visible just beyond the new collar.

11 The Botallack Mine power station at the time of the reopening in 1907. The plant consisted of three vertical gas engines driving alternators.

12 The busy scene on the surface at the time of the reopening of Botallack, about 1908. From left to right are: the new mill for the crushing and concentration of the ore, the small temporary sinking headgear on the central Allen's Shaft, the roof of the power station and, in the foreground, the foundations for the new steam winding engine with the walls of the engine-house being built around it.

13 Assembling the crushing and concentrating plant in the new mill at Botallack, about 1908.

14 Building the new labyrinth of arsenic flues at Botallack Mine, about 1908.

13

14

15 Levant is one of the great tin and copper mines of Cornwall, and it extends for a mile beneath the ocean. This photograph was taken before Pendeen lighthouse was built on the distant headland, and is thought to date from late in the nineteenth century. The small whitewashed engine house, just left of centre in the photograph, contains the very old beam winding engine which, after the mine closed down in 1930, was the first item to be preserved by the Cornish Engines Preservation Society — now the Trevithick Society. This piece of machinery, probably the oldest steam engine in Cornwall, has now passed into the care of the National Trust.

16 A much later photograph of Levant Mine, taken in the first or second decade of this century, showing, from left to right, the house of the old beam winding engine with the headgear on Skip Shaft partly hidden by the chimney stack, the 45 in diameter cylinder Cornish pumping engine, the capstan, and, in the distance, the Cornish stamps engine. As in the case of Botallack Mine, Levant was an exceptionally dry mine, the total amount of water to be pumped being less than 100 gallons per minute!

17 The Levant shafts and engine-
houses viewed from the north-east,
late last century. In the foreground
is the inclined tunnel through
which the ore crushed in the plant
seen in the background was con-
veyed in wagons up to the stamp-
ing plant for fine crushing.

18 Major Richard (Dick) White,
in the top hat, was a legendary
figure in the St Just-Pendeen
area who dominated the affairs of
the great Levant Mine as both its
purser and manager from 1871
until his death in 1909. (The purser
was the secretary of a cost-book
company.) Among other attain-
ments it is said that his particular
brew of punch was so potent that
the smell of it a quarter of a mile
away would knock any man blind
drunk!

19 A later photograph of Major White standing in front of the doorway of the Levant Count House, surrounded by some of the members of the staff.

20 Men at work underground in Levant Mine.

20

21 One of the few examples of ponies being employed underground in Cornwall for hauling waggons of ore. This photograph was taken at Levant Mine and was probably at the 278 fathom level which extends for a mile beneath the sea.

22 The Dry or miner's change house at Levant Mine where the men washed and changed and their underground clothes were dried above hot pipes seen about the turn of the twentieth century.

23

24

23 Left of centre is the short headgear on Skip Shaft where all the ore was hoisted at Levant, and on the right is the Cornish pumping engine and its boiler house. In the right-hand foreground can be seen the old fashion hand capstan for lifting heavy pump parts in the Engine or pumping shaft. The two shafts were sunk so close to one another that there were only a few feet of rock between them.

24 The old Cornish stamps for crushing the ore and the rotative beam engine which drove them at Levant, probably photographed late in the nineteenth century.

25 The headgear on Guide Shaft at the Higher Bal section of Levant Mine and the rotative beam engine which did both the winding and pumping photographed early this century. It is said to have been a very economical engine to work.

26 A late photograph of Levant Mine taken in 1919 a few days before the man-engine disaster which resulted in the death of thirty-one miners. The mine was partially re-equipped with new plant and struggled on for a few more years but finally succumbed to the disasterous fall in the price of tin in the world-wide slump of 1930. After a lapse of many years the old mine was absorbed by the neighbouring Geevor Tin Mines Ltd, and that company is now re-opening Levant and in order to do so has sunk a major flat incline shaft below the deepest workings of Geevor. Apart from the fact that the new incline commences at the bottom of an existing mine instead of at the surface it is somewhat reminiscent of the celebrated Diagonal Shaft at Botallack Mine.

27

27   Miners at the Wheal Carne section of the Geevor Tin Mine photographed in the early part of the present century.

28   The old beam winding and pumping engines of the Carn Galver tin mine standing by the side of the coastal road between Zennor and Morvah. The old

photograph is believed to have been taken about 1880. The ruins of these old buildings are still standing.

29   Rebuilding the stack of Wheal Mary pumping engine after it had been struck by lightning on the last day of March, 1886. Wheal Mary formed a part of the exten-

sive Wheal Sisters tin mines about 2 miles south of St Ives.

30   A group of mine captains outside Wheal Sisters Count House or mine office, probably in 1886.

28

29

30

31 The Giew tin mine was worked beneath the granite of Trink Hill, 2 miles SSW of St Ives. This was one of a group of old mines re-opened by the St Ives Consolidated Mines Ltd in 1908, but it was the only one that was successful. It continued in production until 1923 but the very low price of tin then prevailing brought the enterprise to an end. The photograph, probably taken about 1912, shows Frank's Shaft, the principal one at Giew Mine. From left to right are the power station, the old pumping engine-house (then used as an ore bin), the headgear and winding engine and air compressor house.

32 A small wooden headgear on one of the lesser shafts at Giew Mine, about 1909. This shows clearly how rock and ore were raised in iron 'Kibbles'.

33 An electric winding engine at Giew Mine, about 1909.

34 The old fashioned dressing floors where the tin ores were concentrated, at the St Ives Consols Mines, three-quarters of a mile south-west of the centre of St Ives. This photograph was probably taken in the 1870s, and shows how labour intensive the process was.

35

36

35 It is not often realized that during the nineteenth century Cornwall was one of the foremost industrialized regions of England. To serve the needs of the mining industry three large and several smaller engineering works were established, the largest and most important of them all being that of Harvey & Co Ltd at Hayle who were noted for their massive beam pumping engines. This photograph shows a large cast-iron beam (or bob as they were known in Cornwall) in the works with the Hayle railway viaduct beyond, probably in the 1890s.

36 Another notable Harvey product, the pneumatic stamps for the fine crushing of tin and other ores, this set being made in 1888.

37 In addition to mining machinery Harvey & Co became involved in heavy engineering in general and also in shipbuilding. This

37

38

picture shows their largest vessel, the steamer *Ramleh*, of just under 4,000 tons net and built in 1891, just before leaving the fitting-out berth, with Harvey & Co's boiler shops in the background.

38 Wheal Lucy was a small tin mine in the sandhills north of Hayle. The photograph shows the chimney-stack and a part of an old beam engine-house which had been incorporated in a smaller building for a horizontal steam engine providing power for both pumping and winding.

39 The valley of the River Hayle, south of St Erth, contains a shallow alluvial tin deposit which was worked during the late 1920s. The excavating was done by means of a small steam shovel which is believed to have been one of the last steam-driven shovels made in the world before the all-conquering diesel engine supplanted steam power.

39

40

41

40 The Tregurtha Downs tin mine a mile north-east of Marazion photographed late last century. This was a very wet mine and the beautiful 80 in diameter cylinder Cornish pumping engine, seen on the left, often had to run at exceptional speed in winter time. After the mine closed down the engine was purchased by the South Crofty Company and re-erected at their mine between Redruth and Camborne in 1903. This gave wonderful service until 1955 when it was replaced by electric pumps, being the last Cornish pumping engine to work on a Cornish mine. The engine was then preserved by the Cornish Engines Preservation Society and later handed over to the National Trust. That body had in mind a scheme for bringing the engine back to Tregurtha Downs and erecting it in its old engine-house (which still stands) to form the nucleus of a working mining museum to be established there. If this was done it would probably be the only time in the long history of the Cornish pumping engine that one of them was erected twice in the same building! Unfortunately this scheme is being held in abeyance for the time being for financial reasons.

41 The very ancient and important Great Work Mine worked in the saddle of high land between the summits of Godolphin and Tregonning Hills, about 4 miles WNW of Helston. This photograph was probably taken towards the end of the nineteenth century, when the mine was still working on a small scale, and shows the summit of Godolphin Hill in the distance. The ruins of the pumping engine house and stack on the Leeds Shaft, seen near the left-hand edge of the picture, can still be seen for many miles around as they are 400 ft above sea level. Hamilton Jenkin has recorded that there are references to the mine as early as 1540 and as long ago as 1584 it was employing at least 300 persons continually.

42 Some of the tin dressing plant at the small Lady Gwendoline Mine which was worked on the western extension of the Great Work lodes earlier in the present century.

43 Wheal Vor, a mile north of Breage (and 3 miles north-west of Helston) was one of the greatest and richest tin mines ever discovered in Cornwall; at one time its output amounted to about a third of all the tin being mined in the county. Work probably commenced there in the fifteenth century and there were several different periods of activity, the greatest being in the years 1812-47. In 1906 a new company was formed to drain the mine and explore the ground further eastward. The work was centred at Borlase's Shaft, using one of the first electrically driven sinking pumps to be employed in Cornwall, power being generated by the company's own steam-driven plant. The photograph shows the surface equipment as it then appeared. Unfortunately, after the mine had been largely unwatered the breakage of a single bolt led to the complete smash of the generating plant and as the shareholders were unwilling to spend any more money on the venture the mine was again abandoned.

44 An interior view of the Wheal Vor generating plant from the steam engine end of the building, about 1907.

45 The Wheal Vor power plant from the electrical end.

46 In the valley south of Wheal Vor a small plant was erected to re-treat the refuse and sand 'tails' from Wheal Vor as well as working some of the shallow parts of the Wheal Metal Mine. This was officially termed Wheal Metal and Flow but was known locally as Gold Hill. This photograph showing the machinery was probably taken in the early years of the present century.

47 The 'Old Men's' Shaft at the Basset and Grylls Mine at Porkellis, near Wendron, 4 miles north-east of Helston. There have been several periods of working of this mine, the last one ending in 1938. The photograph was taken about 1908 when the mine was being re-opened.

48

49

48 Parbola Mine, 3 miles south-west of Camborne, was also known as Wheal Jennings. An unusual type of tin deposit was worked here up until 1884 and early in the present century the mine was reopened. In the latter working gas engines provided the power and the old Cornish engine-house was used for other purposes. The picture shows the mine as it appeared about 1907-8.

49 A grinding pan was used for the fine crushing of the tin ore at Parbola when the mine was last worked. The photograph shows the large doorway of the old Cornish engine house through which the steam cylinder and other large parts of the old beam engine entered the building.

50 The rubber belt 'vanners' used for concentrating the tin ore at Parbola when the mine was last worked.

51 An interior view of the Roseworthy Hammer Mills, 1¼ miles west of Camborne, where the long handle Cornish shovels were made for the mines. The wheel on the right, driven by a large waterwheel outside the building, had a number of projections around its periphery which struck the end of the rocking beam thus tilting it and lifting the heavy iron hammer head at the other end of the beam. As soon as it was released the hammer fell under its own weight striking the anvil block a heavy blow. A piece of hot iron placed on the anvil could thus be beaten to the desired shape.

52 An exterior view of the Hammer Mills showing the waterwheels which worked the tilt hammers. Unfortunately, the whole site has since been levelled and there is no longer any indication that a most interesting small industry once existed there.

50

51

52

53

53 Another view of one of the tilt hammers at Roseworthy forging a piece of red-hot iron or steel held by the smith with his tongs while his mate controls the hammer.

54 Standing in the fields north of the A30 road at Roseworthy, a large isolated chimney stack can be seen which is a reminder of the arsenic refinery that once existed there. The 'arsenic soot' or crude arsenic received from the mines was here burnt again with a smokeless fire and condensed in a labyrinth of brick-built chambers. When these were opened the highly poisonous snow-white refined arsenic could be shovelled out as shown in the picture. Note the Cornish type of miner's wheelbarrow in use.

55 A general view inside the refinery showing the condensing chambers or flues on the right-hand side with iron plates luted with clay to keep in the deadly fumes while the furnace was in operation. The man is carefully sealing the barrels containing the deadly and very heavy powder. The barrel lying on its side has stencilled on its end 'English Arsenic Company'. In all these photographs it will be noted that the men use crude respirators of cotton wool inserted in the nostrils, to prevent them breathing in the fine arsenic dust, but it is said that through long exposure to it the body became inured to the poison. Nevertheless, it was essential for the arsenic men to keep very clean, washing frequently and avoiding as far as possible any sweating otherwise serious skin trouble could result. Safer and more controllable poisonous substances are now available and the market for arsenic has virtually disappeared, but at one time it was a valuable by-product of some of the Cornish mines.

54

55

56

56 The refined arsenious oxide was next ground to a fine powder in a machine driven by a waterwheel and passed down through a spout into small barrels, one of which can be seen on the floor beneath the man.

Redruth — St Agnes — Perranzabuloe

This area lies east and north of the town of Redruth and comprises the parishes of Gwennap, St Day, Chacewater, Kea, St Agnes and Perranzabuloe.

Gwennap was famous for the Consolidated Mines, which was an amalgamation of numerous small mines worked with success from 1819, for the neighbouring United Mines, and for Tresavean Mine, all large producers of copper ore; Tresavean Mine produced tin at depth. Mining in the area goes back several centuries, and according to some, St Paul preached to the tinners of St Day. East of Gwennap lies Kea, where Wheal Jane and numerous small mines are situated, while further north, near Chacewater, lie Killifreth Mine and Great Wheal Busy, the last-named an important copper producer early in the eighteenth century. From Redruth north-eastwards to Perranzabuloe a broad strip of country contains a large number of small mines, many of considerable antiquity. Among the more important concerns were Wheal Peevor, near Scorrier, whose three engine-houses form a prominent landmark, Wheal Kitty, in St Agnes, West Wheal Kitty, and Blue Hills Mine. These were all worked in the last century for tin, while Wheal Kitty worked as late as 1930. Further east was West Chiverton Mine, which worked for lead and zinc. Numerous small workings, some of which worked into the present century, are to be found around Perranporth, while the Great Perran Iron Lode was worked at Treamble, where the great excavation there is now used as a caravan site.

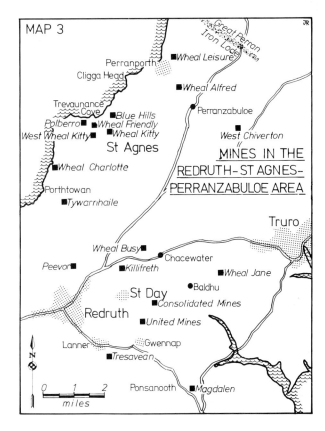

MAP 3

MINES IN THE REDRUTH–ST AGNES–PERRANZABULOE AREA

57

57 In 1907 the famous old Tresavean copper mine at Lanner was reopened in the expectation of finding tin beneath the once very rich and profitable deposits of copper ore, and to a limited extent this proved to be the case. Instead of installing a Cornish engine again in the old engine house it was decided to put in a steam-driven electric generating plant in the building and to drain the mine with electric pumps. In order to secure adequate draught for the large new boilers the old chimney stack was heightened to a total of 150ft — the tallest mine stack in Cornwall. The boilers stood in the low building by the side of the engine-house, seen here about 1909-10.

58

58 The three high-pressure Lancashire boilers for steaming the generating engines.

59 One of the high-speed pressure-lubricated compound engines driving an alternator about 1911. Later, the company took an electric power supply from the public mains and this particular engine was cleverly converted to an air compressor by changing the steam cylinders for new air compression cylinders and substituting an electric motor for the alternator.

60 By 1914 Tresavean Mine had been equipped with a very powerful steam winding engine, taking steam from the boilers that had previously driven the generating engines. The white winding engine house can be seen on the left of the picture. The mill and dressing plant had also been erected, as seen right of centre. The first tin was sold in 1914 and the mine continued until 1928 by which time it was 2,660 ft deep — the second deepest mine in Cornwall. Unfortunately,

the tin values fell off in depth and the mine closed in 1928.

61 A water turbine driving a small set of Cornish stamps and other tin recovery plant at the small Magdalen Mine just east of Posanooth, possibly about 1913-14.

TRESAVEAN MINE.

60

61

62

63

62 At the turn of the century a powerful steam-driven Cornish stamps and dressing plant was erected in the centre of the old United copper mines at Gwennap. The intention was to treat all the dumps in the area and to extract the tin which they contained. Unfortunately, with the tin recovery techniques then available this was not successful and the plant only worked for a very short while. The photograph of 1902-3 shows the rubber belt vanners of the plant which stood within a few yards of the present car racing track on the United Downs. The new-looking house of the beam engine which drove the stamps still stands there.

63 The old engine house at Shears's Shaft on the Cusvey section of the Consolidated Mines, standing high on the hillside above Twelve Heads.

64 In 1907 the old Wheal Jane Mine near Baldhu was reopened together with a number of adjacent old mines under the title of Falmouth Consolidated Mines Ltd. At that time the work was principally centred at Wheal Jane itself, whereas the recent operations have been mostly at West Wheal Jane. This photograph, taken in about 1908, shows from left to the centre of the picture, the power station (partly obscured by the mill) the mill, and Giles's Shaft, the main one of the mine.

65 The original ball mills at the Wheal Jane plant which were not a success and were soon replaced by Californian stamps.

66

GENERAL VIEW OF WORKS, FACING WEST, CARNON, FALMOUTH CONSOLIDATED LTD. 70.

67

6 A large portable engine at Wheal Jane, probably supplying steam for a pump, about 1908.

7 An auxiliary tin dressing plant owned by Falmouth Consolidated Mines Ltd in the Carnon Valley, situated a little way below Bissoe (now the site of a rubbish dump). The photograph is interesting as showing on the extreme left the track of the old 4ft gauge Redruth and Chasewater Railway and, in the distance, one of the famous wooden viaducts of the Great Western Railway's Falmouth branch line. This picture was taken about 1908 or a little later.

68

8 Hawke's Shaft of the Killifreth tin mine between Scorrier and Chacewater. The ruined engine-house with its very tall and slender stack is still a prominent feature of the landscape. The photograph was taken soon after a short-lived attempt to rework the mine after World War I, but the plant remained there for many years before being broken up for scrap during World War II. This mine is generally regarded as being one of the best prospects for tin in Cornwall.

69 When it was proposed to re-open the Great Wheal Busy copper, tin and arsenic mine near Chacewater in 1907, there was great rejoicing in the village, for it meant much work for a district where there was not much employment. A bullock was given by Lord Falmouth and roasted whole as a part of the festivities as shown in this picture.

69

70 The primary purpose of re-opening Wheal Busy was to obtain a ready supply of arsenic for an Anglo-Belgian chemical manufacturing company. It was thus necessary to install, among other plant, a calciner for roasting the arsenical ore and brick condensing chambers and flues leading to a tall chimney stack. This photograph shows the stack at its completion, about 1907-8.

71 Before any steam power was available at Wheal Busy, hoisting was performed by means of a horse whim, a vertical-spindle winding drum rotated by a horse walking around in a circular path. This was the way in which winding was performed in most Cornish mines when they were shallow. This photograph dates from about 1907.

STACK GREAT WHEAL BUSY MINE NR. CHACEWATER

72 A general view of the Wheal Busy milling plant containing twenty-five head of Californian stamps and tables, etc, and nearer to the camera, the arsenic roasting plant, condensing chambers and chimney stack, about 1908.

GREAT WHEAL BUSY MINE NEAR CHACEWATER.

71

GREAT WHEAL BUSY MINE NR. CHACEWATER.

72

73 Originally it had been intended to unwater Wheal Busy by means of an electric pump and a gas engine-driven generating plant was therefore installed to provide the power. The early type of centri-fugal pump employed was, how-ever, a complete failure and it was therefore decided to erect a power-ful Cornish engine in the old engine-house which still stood there from a previous working of the mine. The engine, which had originally worked on a Cornish mine near Par and had then gone to a colliery in South Wales, was purchased and brought back to Cornwall in 1909 for re-erection

"ERECTION OF BOB" CORNISH PUMP ENGIN HOUSE GREAT WHEAL BUSY MINE

at Wheal Busy. The photograph shows the massive 35 ton beam, made of rolled iron plates about 4in thick, being inched towards the house prepared for its reception.

74   The engine house at Wheal Busy with the beam up in place showing the big pulley blocks used for lifting, and the timbers up above which bore the weight while the lift was in progress.

75 The Wheal Busy 85 in diameter cylinder pumping engine completed and at work in 1910. The picture shows, on the left, the new boiler house containing three Lancashire boilers and, on the right, a part of the balance bob. Note the man in the kibble high above the beam. It is a point of interest that it was at Wheal Busy in 1778 that James Watt erected his first pumping engine in Cornwall — the precursor of the true 'Cornish beam engine' as it came to be known all over the world.

76 Unfortunately, the Anglo-Belgian Company appears to have been always short of capital and the working of the mine was an intermittent affair. Finally, the plant was taken over by the adjoining Killifreth Company and in 1923-4 Wheal Busy was again active for a short while as arsenic was then fetching a high price. This was the last time that the fine old pumping engine worked and shortly after the end of World War II she was broken up for scrap after having stood in the house for so many years unused. This sad picture, taken in 1952, shows the lower part of the cylinder smashed with dynamite, the piston rod blown to one side and the piston rings lying on the floor.

77

78

77 At the turn of the century a very great advance in ore dressing was achieved by the development of the flotation process by which a great part of the world's minerals are now recovered. It is therefore a matter of considerable historic interest that one of the earliest experimental flotation plants, using the Elmore oil vacuum process, was erected at the Tywarnhaile copper mine near Porthtowan. This photograph of the plant under erection is thought to have been taken in or about 1901.

78 The old waterwheel-driven corn mill at Porthtowan. Many miners in the olden days were also small farmers or fishermen and it was little mills such as this which served the needs of the community in the days when mining was at its height throughout the length and breadth of Cornwall.

WHEAL CHARLOTTE MINE NR. ST. AGNES

79 Wheal Charlotte, with the surface employees, a couple of miners and two lady visitors gathered around the plant, about 1910-12. A typical example of the so-called 'good old days' when everything was simple, when most men could turn their hands to a number of trades, and there was the minimum of paper work; wages were low, but so was the cost of living in Cornwall!

80

81

80 Wheal Charlotte was a small tin mine on the eastern side of the Chapel Combe valley which runs inland from the coast at Chapel Porth, near Porthtowan. This must not be confused with the very much larger copper mine, sometimes referred to as Great Wheal Charlotte, which is on the cliffs just west of Chapel Porth. The little mine shown in this photograph was being worked about 1912, partly by means of an adit level driven into the hillside and also from a flat inclined shaft sunk further up the hill. Note the small steam-driven set of Cornish stamps and the round 'buddles' for separating the tin from the waste.

81 Wheal Peevor, about a mile north-east of Redruth, was in its day a very rich tin mine. The photograph was probably taken about 1890, by which time the mine was idle. This picturesque group of three engine-houses, now roofless, can be seen from the new by-pass road when approaching Redruth from the east.

82 The Cornish stamps beam engine at the Wheal Kitty mine at St Agnes whose house was destroyed by fire in 1905; it was thought to have been due to arson by an official of the mine who had been sacked. The house was rebuilt and the engine worked again for some years. This photograph shows very clearly how the power from the steam engine was transferred from the steam cylinder on the left to the crank and flywheels on the right via the overhead rocking beam or bob, which pivoted on bearings on top of the massive bob-wall — virtually the only part of the engine house left standing.

83

84

3 An old and damaged, but interesting photograph showing the building of the pumping engine-house at Sara's Shaft of Wheal Kitty at St Agnes in 1910. Note that although the roof timbers are in place the brick upper part of the stack has not yet been built. Most unusually, the beam of the engine is already partly in the house with its rear end protruding through the wide 'cylinder opening' or large doorway. This was the last Cornish engine to work in the St Agnes district and did not finally stop until 1930.

4 Miners leaving the cage in Sara's Shaft at Wheal Kitty in, it is believed, 1919. Note on the right two large 'kibbles' for raising ore and stone.

5 In consequence of the difficulties arising from World War I, Wheal Kitty had to suspend operations in 1919, but the mine was reopened in 1926 and much

85

new plant installed. The photograph was taken in about 1928 and shows on the left the new mill, in the centre Sara's Shaft and pumping engine and on the right the winding engine and new compressor and boiler house, new stack etc. A new and very rich tin lode was cut at the bottom of the mine but it was closed down in the world-wide slump in 1930.

86 West Wheal Kitty, on the western side of the Trevaunance Valley, was one of the richest and most profitable tin mines ever worked in the St Agnes area. The photograph shows a group of West Kitty miners outside their 'dry' or change house. Note the very large bunch of miner's candles carried by the man on the left. This was probably for a large 'pare' (or gang) of men working together in one part of the mine.

87 The Wheal Friendly section of West Kitty Mine, probably a few years before World War II. This now roofless engine-house still stands high above the deep Trevaunance Valley on its western side.

88 Both the old and new steam driven stamps and tin-dressing plant of West Kitty at 'Jericho',

about a mile east of St Agnes. All the ore from the mine which was worked under the town, had to be transported here by horses and carts.

89 The seaward end of the Travaunance Valley at St Agnes. The old buildings in the foreground are said to have been originally an iron foundry, possibly

the Trevaunance Foundry which is recorded as having been sold up in 1865. Later the place housed a part of the tin recovery plant seen in the photograph. In the background is the old St Agnes harbour where most of the coal used in the local mines was brought in by means of small sailing vessels.

88

89

90 The most recent mine to work in St Agnes was the Turnavore Shaft of Polberro Tin Ltd, which was reopened in 1937 and deepened from 650ft to 1,090ft thus making it the deepest shaft in the St Agnes district. This work was done in the hope of intersecting the rich West Kitty and Wheal Kitty lodes which were abandoned when Wheal Kitty was closed down in the world-wide slump of 1930. The first-named lode was indeed cut and a good deal of work done on it, but the acute man power and other diffi-culties which developed during World War II prevented output from being built up to an economic level and although tin was then being produced it became impos-sible to continue and the mine was closed early in 1941. This was a very great pity for soon afterwards the Allies lost the great eastern tin-producing countries and then every ton of tin that could be mined in Cornwall was of the ut-most importance to Britain's war effort. In this, the last working of the Turnavore Shaft, the plant was all electrically driven, but the old engine-house was converted into a miner's change house. The smoke from the old stack came from a small heating boiler used to pro-vide hot washing water etc, and not from large steam boilers as previously.

91 Long after regular mining ceased at the old Polberro Mine at St Agnes tributers continued to work there on a small scale above water level. The picture shows one of their 'horse whims' for raising their ore to surface, early this century. *(Photo: Albert J. Fellows)*

92 A fine photograph of the old
Blue Hills Mine at the seaward end
of the Trevellas Valley, St Agnes,
probably taken in about 1890. In
the centre is the 70 in cylinder
Cornish pumping engine at the
Engine Shaft and, to the left, the
big flywheel of the horizontal
single-cylinder engine driving the
stamps and also winding from
several shafts.

that the cylinder opening, or large doorway, had to be in the side of the house thus making for a weak wall with so many other openings, and the heavy beam probably had to be lifted in at the front end with the weight suspended from the headgear. The whole thing must have been a very awkward erection job and quite unnecessary as there was plenty of room behind the building to bring in the heavy parts if the house had been built in the normal manner. West Chiverton was at one time the most productive and profitable of the Cornish and Devonshire lead mines and employed 1,000 people. It closed down in 1886.

95   Batters' engine-house from the western or boiler-house side. The two small wall openings at the lowest part of the building were for the cylinder steam jacket pipe on the left, and the main steam pipe on the right. The tall doorway still further right was to give access from the boiler house to the driving floor or 'bottom chamber' of the engine house.

96   A very early photograph of Perranporth showing the derelict engine houses of Wheal Leisure and the other extensive copper mines in the area. Even the shape of the small island known as Chapel Rock has changed since the photograph was taken. This is undoubtedly the oldest photograph in this book; it may date from the 1850s, but it is reputed (but unlikely) to be as old as 1840.

93

93   A strange sight even in a land of strange things! The remains of the pumping and winding machinery of a small lead prospect in the shallow valley a mile north of Mithian Church. It was known as Wheal Treasure or the Silverwell Lead Mine, but it was also remarked cynically that 'It did not contain enough lead to make earrings for a black-beetle!' Apparently the old iron chimney (the fire tube from an old boiler) did not provide sufficient draught for this boiler and it was therefore heightened with the top-heavy brickwork seen in the picture. Notwithstanding that two out of three supporting chains had rusted away, the old stack withstood all the gales and it was only demolished during the scrap-iron drive during World War II. The mine was last worked before World War I.

94   A large and most unusual engine-house at Batters' Shaft of the famous West Chiverton lead and zinc mine, half a mile north of the A30 road and 1¼ miles west of Zelah Village. Instead of the stack being built at one of the back corners of the house it was built on the centre line thus completely blocking the back of the building for bringing in the 80 in cylinder and beam. The consequence was

95

96

97

98

97 Twentieth-century mining at Perranporth. The tin and wolfram mine at Cligga Head, a mile west of Perranporth, which was worked on quite an extensive scale during World War II. The photograph shows the erection of the headgear and mill buildings in 1941-2.

98 Prospecting operations taking place early in this century at Bolingey, near Perranporth, which led to the opening up of the Wheal Alfred zinc mine.

99 About 2 miles north-east of Perranporth there is a very large vein of iron ore known as the Great Perran Iron Lode which was extensively worked in the 1870s. Shortly before World War II an attempt was made to work it again at Treamble by opencast methods using the then recently introduced bulldozers and scrapers. Two of these machines can be seen at work in the picture. The venture was not an economic success for the great vein was found to be too irregular

99

in shape to permit working in this way, but some iron ore was obtained during the war-time emergency by using more conventional underground methods.

100 One of the big tractors and scrapers employed on the Great Perran Iron Lode opencast project in 1938.

100

St Austell to the Tamar

One of the two productive uranium mines in Cornwall was at South Terras, at the western end of the St Austell mining and china clay area. The district was one which had only a few large mines, and with the expansion of the china clay industry, mining in the area declined in importance. Stream and shallow surface workings survived to the north, on Goss Moor, into the present century, and a small wolfram mine worked successfully, but not continuously, between 1918 and 1958 at Castle an Dinas. Among the open works to the east was Great Treveddoe Mine, now almost completely obscured by vegetation.

Around Caradon Hill, in the parishes of Linkinhorne and St Cleer, were numerous mines, including the Phoenix Mines. North of Callington, Redmoor Mine was worked by a number of different companies in the last century, while east of it lay Kit Hill Consols, on the hill of that name, and Hingston Down Consols, the last-named later worked with Clitters Mine. The Clitters United company was one which was successful at working complex ores containing several commercially valuable minerals, though the earliest plant built to do this type of ore-dressing was erected over a century ago at New Consols Mine, some two miles to the north-west.

On the south slope of Hingston Down lay the Prince of Wales mine, whose shares, early in the present century, were a popular gamble among the French admirers of King Edward VII. Nearer to Devon lay Okel Tor Mine, which was worked from the middle of the last century, at first for silver-lead, then for copper, and finally for tin and arsenic.

101 Ventonwyn was a small tin mine half a mile north-west of Hewas Water on the Truro to St Austel road, and the old engine-house is a prominent landmark visible from several miles away. This rotative beam engine did the pumping in addition to driving the small battery of Cornish stamps. The interesting thing, however, about this posed photograph dating from early this century is that every man, whether surface or underground, is shown exhibiting the tools of his trade. For example, the fourth man from the left in the front row was the pitman and he is holding a Cornish pump 'bucket'. The man next to him is the sample tryer, he is holding his 'vanning shovel'. The seventh and eighth men from the left (standing) are the blacksmiths with their hammers. The man on the extreme right with the oilcan in his hand is undoubtedly the engine driver. The men with candles fixed with lumps of clay to their hats are, of course, the miners, and so on.

MAP 4 — MINES IN THE St Austell-Tamar Area

02   In the big china clay industry
f Cornwall, centred on St Austell,
1 the days of steam power it was
sual to have a Cornish beam
ngine pumping from each pit with
separate horizontal engine haul-
1g the waste material up the
1clines to the great conical tips
7hich were such a prominent
eature of the landscape. As the
eam engines varied their length of
troke with slight variations of
team pressure in the boilers when
he winding engines were working,
t was very difficult for one driver
o look after two engines simul-
aneously. A local engineer,
Jackie' Menire, therefore invented
7hat was known as the 'St Austell
overnor', for automatically con-
rolling the length of piston stroke
f the beam pumping engines. The
photograph shows one of these
imple but clever devices as applied
o the 50 in cylinder pumping en-
;ine at the Parkandillick clay
vorks at St Dennis. Fortunately,
his engine has been preserved in
vorking order by her owners,
English Clays Lovering Pochin &
Co Ltd.

103 The very last beam pumping engine to work commercially in Cornwall, was the 30 in cylinder engine at the Greensplat clay works, about 2 miles NNW of St Austell. This delightful little engine was originally a rotative one but its flywheel was purchased for another engine at South Greensplat works. It was then decided that, instead of scrapping the remainder of the engine, it should be used as a non-rotative pumping engine and as such it was re-erected at Greensplat in about 1887, and it continued to work there until the 23 February 1959. It bears neither maker's name nor date but is thought may have been made by the St Blazey Foundry. It is certainly very old. The engine remained in its house at Greensplat until 1972 when it was purchased by the Wendron Forge Museum (near Helston) and re-erected as an open-air exhibit where it can be seen working — the actual movement now being performed by means of an hydraulic ram.

104 The 22 in cylinder rotative beam engine at the Great Hallaze clay works about 2 miles north of St Austell, just before World War II. This little engine originally worked at the Devon Gawton copper and arsenic mine on the Devonshire bank of the Tamar River, but in about 1910 it was bought and re-erected at the new clay works, but this was unsuccessful and the engine did not work long there and lay idle in its house for many years. Shortly before World War II it was decided to connect this clay pit with another one by driving a tunnel between the two, thus forming a capacious servoir for public water supply. Electric pumps were at first employed to lower the water level in the pit to enable the tunnel to be driven, but the water was so gritty that there was continual trouble with the pumps. It was then decided to try to work the old engine again and, as rusty and derelict as she appeared to be, this was a great success and enabled the tunnel to be driven. Sadly, after the job had been completed the old engine was broken up for scrap — she deserved a better fate!

105 At Great Hallaze most of the woodwork and floors within the house had gone and temporary planks had to be laid down to enable the driver to move around the engine. A ladder had to be used to oil the 'nose' of the bob and all the boiler fittings had to be replaced; the boiler house had been used as a cattle shed and was half full of hay and straw. No modern diesel or electrical plant would have worked again if they had been subjected to such neglect as had the old steam engine.

106 Bloomdale clay works pumping engine near Foxhole in 1935. This was a much rebuilt 36 in cylinder engine, originally made by the Perran Foundry Company. Previous to being at Bloomdale it had worked at the Polbreen Mine at St Agnes. The man who drove this engine was noted for his encyclopaedic memory for dates. There appeared to have been no local or national happening that he could not give the precise date for no matter how many centuries ago the happening. His memory even extended to most foreign countries, he really was extraordinary! (*Photo: Frank D. Woodhall*)

107 Carpalla clay works 40 in cylinder engine, south of Foxhole. This engine had worked previously on Thomas's Shaft at the celebrated West Wheal Kitty Mine at St Agnes. In 1915 it was removed to Carpalla, being the last beam engine to be erected in the whole of the central clay area of Cornwall. It worked there until replaced by electric pumps in 1944 and was later dismantled and placed in store in London with the intention that it was to be eventually re-erected at the Science Museum. This little engine, of classic form, was built by Harvey & Co of Hayle, who were probably the most famous of the Cornish engine building firms.

108

108 The 50 in cylinder engine at Goonvean clay works, a mile north of St Stephen, seen about 1929. This engine too was made by Harvey & Co of Hayle, in 1863; after working at two mines in St Agnes it was moved to its present site in 1910. In 1928 the beam broke and a new and heavier one was cast by Holman Brothers Ltd of Camborne. This was, probably, the last bob made for a beam engine anywhere in the world. This engine ceased working several years ago but it is still retained in its house by the owners, the Goonvean and Restowrack China Clay Co Ltd, although it is feared that it is now becoming rather rusty.

109 One of the great horse-drawn wagons previously used in the china clay industry.

110 The famous Par Stack of the silver-lead smelting works owned by the Treffry Estate. It is understood to have been built about 1860 and is variously stated to have been 235ft or 280ft high. Whichever dimension is correct, it was undoubtedly the tallest stack built in Cornwall and was said to contain a million bricks. At the time of building it was fashionable for gentlemen to wear very tall top hats and these became known in Cornwall as Par Stacks. The base of the stack stood right by the side of one of the Great Western Railway's tracks and the company was suspicious of the strata on which it was built. Therefore, as it had long been disused, they decided to demolish it in 1907 and the photograph shows the steeplejacks holding aloft the first bricks removed from the top. After it had been reduced to a part of the original height the remainder was thrown towards the sea by an explosive charge on the 23 August 1907. In consequence of its demolition a modern landmark had to be set up to guide shipping as the great chimney had done for so many years.

111 The Goss and Tregoss Moor, north of the great central china clay area, is the largest alluvial tin deposit in Cornwall and has been worked for tin from time immemorial. Unfortunately, the tin which remains is very difficult to recover and a company which was formed to re-work these alluvials burnt its fingers badly when it commenced dredging there in April 1925. The new dredge shown in this photograph was 80ft long with a beam of 35ft and cost £15,000 — then a sizable sum, but it only worked for a short while and was ultimately cut up for scrap.

112 The Castle-an-Dinas wolfram mine was worked beneath the hill of that name, north of Goss Moor, and was a most productive and profitable mine although it only contained one narrow lode or vein. The original workings were on the north side of the hill but by 1941 the mine had extended so far south as to necessitate the sinking of a new shaft on the southern slope of the hill. This unusual photograph was taken from the top of the headgear of the new shaft at Castle-an-Dinas looking down on the big Lancashire boiler and the winding engine during erection in 1942.

113 The narrow but rich lode in the No 5 Level South, at Castle-an-Dinas Mine. The lode is the vertical white quartz vein behind the miner's pick and the spots and black 'figs' in it are lumps and pockets of rich wolfram.

114 One of the open cavities or stopes at Castle-an-Dinas Mine after the ore had been mined. The timber was not required for support of the walls of the stope (which were strong and firm), but for the stage planks on which the miners worked while they drilled their holes for explosives. This was a method of working peculiar to this particular mine and one which enabled the broken ore to be sent to the mill day by day as it was broken. What appears to be a ball of light by the miner's arm was actually a powerful miner's lamp facing the camera.

115

116

5 Great Treveddoe Mine near [V]arleggan was an old tin and cop-[pe]r mine worked below the floor of [a] massive open quarry known as [O]ld Wheal Whisper. On average, [th]e grade of tin ore here was always [lo]w, but as the plant was driven by [w]ater power it was possible to [w]ork the mine very cheaply.

[11]6 An old waterwheel-driven [se]t of Cornish stamps, believed to [b]e at Great Treveddoe Mine.

117 The Phoenix United Mines, one mile north-west of Caradon Hill, closed down in 1898. After producing a lot of copper these mines became the largest tin producers in the eastern half of Cornwall and in their day were very profitable. In 1907 the Phoenix Mines were most unwisely re-opened for it should have been obvious from the records of the nineteenth-century company that the mines had become poor in

depth. However, it was decided to sink a fine new perpendicular shaft equipped with a new 80in cylinder pumping engine and the photo-graph shows the building of the new engine house and the erection of the temporary headgear for the sinking of the shaft.

118 The Prince and Princess of Wales (later King George V and Queen Mary) visited Phoenix in June 1909 when the Prince christened the new shaft 'The Prince of Wales Shaft' and the Princess started the fine new Cornish pumping engine — the last large new one to be built anywhere in the world. The shaft was ultimately sunk to a depth of 1,200 ft, the mine drained to the bottom and a certain amount of development done below the bottom of the old workings. This, however, only exposed small patches of good ore and the mines were again abandoned in 1914. The photograph shows the fine new plant at the Prince of Wales Shaft as it appeared in about 1909. On the hillside in the background can be seen the Cheeswring granite quarry with the famous Cheeswring pile of rocks on the skyline on the edge of the quarry.

119 The cover of the 80 in diameter cylinder of the new Phoenix pumping engine built by Holman Brothers Ltd of Cambourne in 1907. After the mine closed again in 1914 the engine was greased over and remained in its house until about 1931 when it was, most regrettably, broken up for scrap. This is said to have been a good engine and would run up to nine strokes per minute with ease.

120 The unusual steel plate beam of the new Phoenix Mines' pumping engine in 1909. Unfortunately, the bright sunlight coming through the window over the beam has rather spoilt the photograph.

121 The fine new steam winding engine also built by Holman Brothers Ltd in 1907 for the Prince of Wales Shaft of the Phoenix Mines. When they closed down again this engine was sold for further service at a colliery.

120

121

122 When the Phoenix Mines were last worked the old custom of the mine barber seems to have been revived whereby for a small monthly sum of money the men could have a haircut and a weekly shave.

123 At about the same time as the Phoenix Mines were being re-opened in 1907 the smaller South Phoenix Mine was being further examined and the photograph shows the plant as it then existed, but the venture was not a success.

124 A small electric winding engine at South Phoenix Mine, about 1908.

125 Immediately east of Kit Hill and within a mile and a half of the River Tamar is the high ridge of land known as Hingston Down. At the highest point, 880ft above sea level, is the Hingston Down Consols tin and copper mine which was reopened early in the present century in conjunction with the Gunnislake Clitters Mine on the Cornish bank of the Tamar. To pump the water at Hingston Down Mine a rotative beam engine was purchased from the Devon Great Consols copper and arsenic mine which had then recently closed. This photograph of 1903 shows the new engine house at Hingston with the bob or beam up in place, and the big flywheel being re-assembled. With the aid of a strong glass the name of the maker of the engine can be read on the bob on the original photograph, namely 'Bedford Foundry, Tavistock'. This engine-house, with its roof hidden by parapet walls, still stands as a prominent landmark on the summit of Hingston Down.

126 Hingston Down Consols seen when working in the early years of the twentieth century. Unfortunately, the shaft in which the pump worked proved to be a bad and crooked one and much trouble was experienced with the plant. Electric power was then generated in the buildings seen on the right of the picture but the early type electric pumps employed also gave a lot of trouble and in the end it was the Cornish pump on which the company had to rely.

127 The mill for the treatment of the ores from the Hingston and Clitters Mines was on the steep hillside immediately below the latter mine and above the Tamar which can be seen in its twisting course on the right-hand side of the photograph.

126

127

128 A photograph of the plant in the Clitters mill, possibly about 1903.

129 Tables etc, in Clitters mill.

130 At the village of Luckett, $2\frac{1}{2}$ miles further up the Tamar valley than the site of the Clitters mill, there is an old and interesting mine which had produced a good deal of copper and arsenic ores and a certain amount of tin. It has been variously named Wheal Martha, New Consols and New Great Consols and it has had a very varied but intermittent career between 1838 and 1952. Although the dumps were worked on a considerable scale during World War I for tin, Wolfram and arsenic, underground operations ceased as long ago as 1879, leaving a mass of old-fashioned mining machinery rusting away until it was broken up for scrap shortly before World War II. The photograph shows some of the old engines as they appeared about 1938 shortly before being scrapped. From left to right they are the 80 in cylinder pumping engine on Phillips' or the Engine Shaft, the remains of a rotative beam engine which drove the Cornish rolls for crushing the copper ore, and the beam winding engine whose house was nearly covered with ivy. This was so old

130

that it had chains on its drums instead of wire ropes. It has been said that the whole mine was an industrial site of unique interest and it is a great pity that this machinery was scrapped. In 1946 the mine was reopened and drained to the bottom by means of electric pumps. A further 170 ton of black tin, ie tin oxide, was produced and a little wolfram, but it was not a successful venture and the mine closed again in December 1952.

131 The very old Cornish pumping engine and its most unusual house at New Consols. The building originally contained a 50in cylinder engine and when more power and an altogether larger engine (which had a different length of stroke) was needed the house was not suitable. Furthermore, because of the position of the chimney stack at the back of the building, the large doorway through which the cylinder enters could not be sufficiently enlarged to bring in the new 80in cylinder. In order to avoid the cost and time of building an entirely new engine house the difficulty was ingeniously overcome in the following manner: the thick 'bob end' (ie the thick wall which bears the weight of the rocking beam) was demolished and replaced by a thicker wall at the requisite distance from the mine shaft. As the new masonry might not bond sufficiently strongly with the old, the new wall was extended with a buttress on each side, so as to give it extra strength, and these side extensions were covered with small gable roofs. Furthermore, the wall opening for the 'plug door' under the beam, which is always made as small as possible so as not to weaken the wall under the weight of the beam and its load, was made sufficiently large to enable the large cylinder to be brought into the house that way. After the cylinder was in place a false arch of brickwork was built inside the large opening thus strengthening the whole wall. This photograph was taken in 1938 just as the dismantling of the engine commenced.

132 At New Consols, in addition to all the other engines, there was on the southern side of the valley also a large Cornish stamps engine complete with the stamps and several calciner furnaces for roasting the arsenical ores. The picture shows the stamps engine in the 1920s with its two odd size flywheels and the auxiliary beam for pumping the 'dressing' or processing water required for the treatment of the tin ore. The engine itself was of unusual design with cam and roller valve motion and with the valves at the side of the cylinder instead of in front as is usual. In common with all the other engines on the mine, this one still had its old Cornish boilers in situ, but in each case the boiler-house roof had collapsed.

133 Watson's Shaft at the Prince of Wales Mine at Harrowbarrow, on the southern side of the Hingston Down ridge. This early twentieth-century photograph is interesting as showing the 'hollow-work' or cast iron trellis-like bob of the 50in cylinder pumping engine. This type of engine beam was rather rare and this one was the last of the type to work in Cornwall — the mine closed in 1916. Note also the very old type of portable steam engine on the left pulling a skip up an incline with material to fill an old working which had caved in from down below and was in dangerous proximity to the engine-house. The automatic tipping arrangement of the skip is of interest.

134 A close-up view of the pumping engine and headgear on Watson's Shaft at the Prince of Wales Mine. The hollow-work bob of the engine can be clearly seen in this photograph, as also can the timber surface balance-beam. The bell high above the engine-house was a survivor of earlier days before the steam whistle or hooter was in use to tell the men the time when the shifts began or ended — few owned a watch in those days! A mine in Cornwall was called a 'bal' and hence this bell on every mine was always referred to as the 'bal bell'. The Prince of Wales Mine was owned latterly by a very impecunious company and its abandonment was due to special circumstances. It is generally thought to be a very good prospect for tin if worked on modern lines.

133

134

Index

The entries refer to illustration
numbers.